Origins

Heroine in Hiding

Tony Bradman ✳ Jonatronix

OXFORD
UNIVERSITY PRESS

Chapter 1 – Dani Day's Story

Full name: Daniella Marie Day
Date of birth: 14th May 1988
Education: Greenville University Degree (first class) in Nano Technology

Greenville High School

Advanced level top grades in:

Physics, Astronomy, Pure Mathematics, Biochemistry, Communication Technology, English, History and French

Employment: Junior Scientist at NICE (The National Institute for Creation of Energy)

Other interests: Hiking, scuba diving, listening to rock music, playing computer games, reading comics

Ambitions: To make the world a better place

To make her father proud

To meet Kurt Morrison (lead singer of The Power)

Hi, I'm Dani.

Dani worked hard at her job as a junior scientist for NICE. She often stayed late in to the evening to finish an experiment or to write up her notes. Then, one evening, a visitor came to the lab …

"Evening Dani," said a voice that made her jump. "Good to see you working hard. Your father would have been proud."

The voice belonged to Dr X – one of the chief scientists at NICE. Rumour had it that he'd shouted his way to the top.

"Er … thank you, Dr X," said Dani.

"Dani," he said. "Your intelligence is wasted up here. How would you like to join my team? We're working on a very special project down in the basement. It's top secret. And believe me … it will change the world!"

Dani gasped. This was the kind of thing she'd dreamed of since she was a little girl.

"Yes!" she cried out. She didn't need to think about it. "I'd love to!"

The very next day, Dani went to work down on Floor X.

"Welcome to Nano Science and Technology Inc!" cried Dr X.

"We call it NASTI," whispered a tall, thin man.

"Yeah, 'cos the boss is real NASTI," chuckled a short, plump man.

"Socket, Plug, this is Dani," said Dr X calmly. "She's here to help us so … BE NICE!"

He turned to Dani and gave her a big smile.

Dani looked around the room. It was some sort of underground laboratory. There were computer display screens on the walls. A strange ball-shaped machine hung in the centre of the room.

Dr X pushed a button and the machine buzzed into life. A bright green X glowed on its surface. Dr X gently pulled out a shiny silver box from the middle of the machine. He turned and twisted the lid and the silver box opened with a soft hiss.

"Take one," he said to Dani, passing her the box.

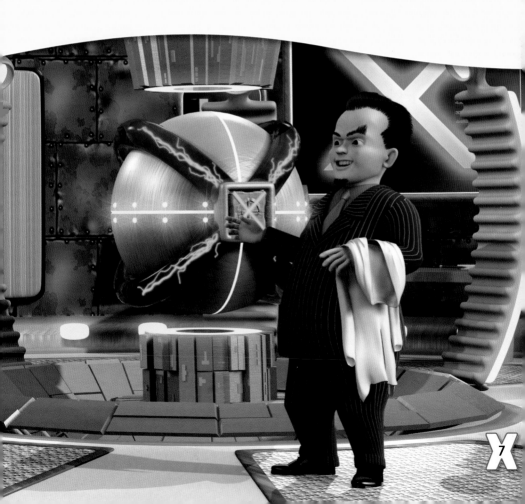

Inside the box were five coloured watches. Dani picked out a purple one and put it on.

"Now," said Dr X. "All you have to do is turn the dial, push the X and …"

Dani did exactly what Dr X told her to do. As she pushed the X something strange happened. She began to shrink. Then the shrinking stopped and she began to grow. She grew taller and taller until she thought her head would hit the ceiling. But then the watch fizzed and crackled and … in a flash, Dani shrank to the size of a mouse.

"Cool!" was all Dani could think to say.

Dani turned the watch again and grew back to her normal size. She was so excited that she didn't notice the shouting at first.

"NO! NO! NO!" Dr X was screaming. "THEY NEED TO BE PERFECT!"

"What's perfect boss?" said the man called Plug.

"GET OUT!" Dr X yelled at them.

Dr X turned to Dani and smiled. There was something not very nice about this smile.

Then Dr X explained his plan to her. He told her that the watches formed the core of his powerful new invention – the X-machine. He also told her how he planned to use the machine to take over the world …

"These watches must be perfect," he said at last. "And you, clever Dani, will work night and day until you make that happen!"

Dani was too shocked to speak. It had all been a trap. What was she to do?

"Make your father proud," chuckled Dr X as he slammed the door behind him. With a loud *CLUNK* the door locked and Dani was left alone.

Chapter 2 – Going in to hiding

Dani tried to open up the X-machine. It was sealed shut. She tried the computers but without a password, they were useless. She searched the room for a way out. All she could find was an air vent and a pipe that took rubbish away. Then, angry with herself for being so stupid, she kicked at a metal waste-paper bin. It gave her an idea.

All the rubbish pipes in NICE took waste straight to the collection bins at the back of the building. The rubbish was collected every day.

Dani picked up a scrap of paper. On it, she scribbled a note.

She put four of the watches back in their box, keeping the purple watch for herself. Then she put the note in the box and sealed it shut. She slipped the box into the rubbish pipe and pressed a button. *POP!* The silver box was gone.

Keep us secret.
Keep us safe.

Now all Dani had to do was get herself out. There was only one thing for it. She turned the dial on her watch. She pushed the X and …

Dani ran down the air vent. She was glad to be free of NASTI. When she got outside she would go straight to the bank. She would take the money left to her by her father and go somewhere Dr X could never find her.

Thinking of her father made Dani stop running. "Make your father proud," Dr X had laughed at her. Could she do that by running away? Dr X was dangerous!

Dani knew that no one would believe her story. Dr X was a NICE chief scientist and she was only a junior scientist. She would have to hide inside NASTI and watch and wait …

Chapter 3 – Some time later ...

It was another busy morning at NASTI HQ. Dr X was busy doing what Dr X did best – shouting at the people who worked for him.

"He can be such a bossy boots sometimes," Plug muttered.

"Er ... that's probably because he is the boss," said Socket.

Scientists ran around doing Dr X's bidding. Computers hummed, screens glowed, printers chattered and strange machines bleeped. X-bots scuttled everywhere.

Dr X had only one mission – to get his special shrinking watches back. He thumped his fist down on his desk and several screens lit up the walls. On the biggest screen was an image of four children. They were Max, Cat, Ant and Tiger. They were the children who had his watches. They were sitting in their micro-den having fun. They had no idea they were being spied on.

"Those watches are mine!"
Dr X yelled. "It makes me so
angry to see those kids playing
with them. Plug! Socket! Come
over here!"

"Right away, sir!" said Plug
and Socket together.

"I have a job for you two,"
said Dr X. "You're to go along
to Room 101 …"

"Oh, wow, boss!' Socket
interrupted. "Does that
mean you want us to do
something important?"

"We promise we won't let
you down," said Plug.

"Actually, it is an important
job. And it's one even you
idiots can't make a mess of,"
said Dr X with a sneer. "You're
to make sure the X-pod bay is
nice and clean. I want it ready
for the launch of my fabulous
new X-pod."

"Oh, right," said Socket,
disappointed. "Come on, Plug.
Let's go and get our
cleaning stuff."

Dr X turned back to his screens. He pushed a button and a more frightening image appeared. It showed another room inside NASTI filled with rows and rows of black robots. These were the X-bots – robots built by Dr X to track down the children and to get the watches back. This was a new type of X-bot and Dr X had built an army of them!

"The pod is almost ready my beauties," purred Dr X. "We won't fail this time!"

What Dr X didn't know was that he too was being watched. From down in the air vent, where she had made her home, micro-sized Dani Day looked out at him.

Dani had known for some time that four children had found the silver box. She remembered the day she had first seen them on Dr X's screens. Each child was wearing a watch – and they were using them to shrink and have fun!

"Those children have no idea what they've stumbled upon," she had said to herself.

Since then she had watched Dr X closely and waited. When Dr X created his first X-bots she had managed to catch one. She had programmed a holographic message into it. She had no idea if it had reached the children.

Now she gazed at the new army of X-bots in horror. This was bad. This was very bad. It was time to do something and the flying X-pod might be just what she needed …

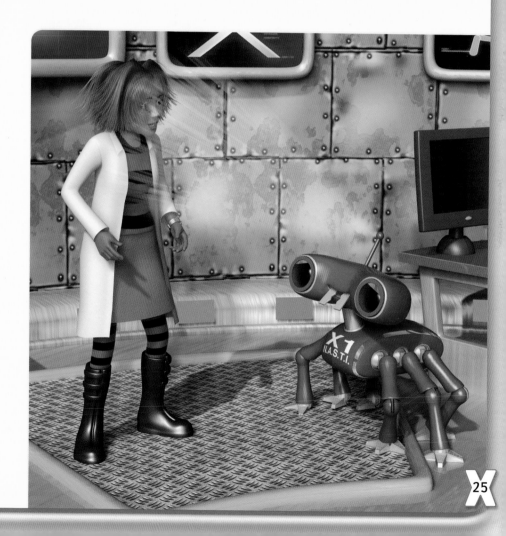

Chapter 4 – The X-pod

Plug and Socket stopped by a cupboard and took out a box of cleaning things. Socket picked out a blue and white apron and put it on.

"Where's my apron?" said Plug.

"Not here," said Socket. "Perhaps you left it back in the control room."

Plug trudged off to get his apron.

"Idiot!" muttered Socket.

Dani was delighted to see Plug return. She scrambled out of her hiding place and climbed into the pocket of Plug's apron just in time. Plug pulled on the apron. Dani felt herself being rocked and swayed. She hoped she wouldn't be crushed by an enormous set of keys and Plug's collection of conkers.

Plug walked down a long corridor. He stopped in front of a large steel door and tapped a code into a keypad on the wall. The door slid back with a loud hiss.

"There you are," said a grumpy Socket. "Come on, give me a hand."

Plug bent down to pick up a cloth. Dani jumped from his pocket. She hid in the box of cleaning things.

She waited for a while then poked her head up to have a look around. What she saw nearly made her eyes pop out. Sitting on a stand in front of her was the fabulous flying X-pod.

"Cool!" was all Dani could think to say to herself.

The X-pod was a flying machine designed for X-bots. But there was space inside for a micro-sized pilot.

Plug and Socket were on the far side of the room making tea. Dani crept over to the stand. She ran up the ramp and climbed into the X-pod. It didn't take her long to get it started. The engine hummed as the X-pod rose into the air …

"Hey, that's not supposed to be happening, is it?" cried Plug.

"Er … no, I don't think so," said Socket, spilling his tea. "Quick, grab it!"

Chapter 5 – Up and away!

Dani boosted the power to the engine and the X-pod rose faster. But not fast enough. She only just managed to steer clear of Socket. The X-pod tumbled over and over as she flew out of reach. She got it back under control. Then, as she swooped past Plug's head, a thought struck her. How was she going to get out of the room?

Socket flapped at the pod with a tea towel, hoping to bring it down. Dani zoomed up and out of the way. And that was when she saw it … there was a small circular door in the ceiling. Swooping past Plug's feather duster she looked down at the controls. Her eyes found a large green button marked EXIT. She hoped it was the right one.

Dani hit the button hard and pointed the X-pod at the door. It opened.

"Yippeee!" cried Dani as she flew the pod up through the door, along a silver tube and out into the clear blue sky.

"We're in so much trouble," said Plug.

"More tea?" said Socket.

Chapter 6 – A warm welcome

Dani could hardly believe that she was outside NASTI. It was so good to be out in the air after all that time spent hiding underground. She swooped through the sky in the X-pod, doing loop-the-loops.

Then, in the middle of a loop, Dani suddenly realized she had no idea where she was going. She wanted to find the four children she had seen on Dr X's screen. She had to warn them about the X-bot army. But she didn't know where to find them.

"Blast!" Dani groaned, cross with herself. She thumped her fist down on the controls. (She had clearly spent too much time watching Dr X.) A computer screen flicked on in front of her. "A computer! That must link to NASTI …" thought Dani.

A few minutes later Dani knew exactly where she could find the children. She tapped the details into the X-pod's navigation system and gave the engines a boost.

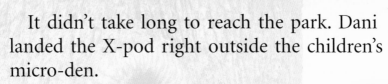

It didn't take long to reach the park. Dani landed the X-pod right outside the children's micro-den.

But as the engines died there was a terrific *CLUNK!* The X-pod rocked. Dani staggered. It was as if the little craft had been hit by a stone. Dani peered out of the window and realized that was exactly what had happened.

Chapter 7 – Dani meets the micro-friends

Max, Cat, Ant and Tiger had been in their den when they heard the buzzing of the X-pod. They looked out to see a mean-looking craft with the word NASTI written across it. They thought they were under attack.

"Run!" Max cried. They hurtled down the stairs just in time to see the X-pod land. Max grabbed some stones and began throwing them at the mysterious craft. The others did the same.

Then the door of the craft opened and a woman with bright pink hair stepped out.

"Hey, stop!" the woman cried. "I'm a friend!"

Tiger ignored her and picked up another stone. But Max stopped him throwing it. The woman was micro-sized … just like them!

"Who are you?" he called out.

"Hey!" cried Ant. "That's the lady in the hologram."

"You got my message?" said the woman in surprise.

"Er … kind of," said Cat.

"It was inside Rover," said Ant. The little red X-bot that Ant had reprogrammed bleeped proudly.

"Who are you?" repeated Max.

"I'm Dani," the woman smiled. "I used to work for Dr X. I had no idea if that X-bot would get through. But I had to try and warn you."

"Warn us? What do you mean, warn us?" snorted Tiger.

Dani had so much to say she didn't know where to start. "Those watches you have …" she began.

"I hope you haven't come to take them off us," Tiger snapped.

"Don't be so rude, Tiger!" hissed Cat.

"You'd better come inside," said Max.

Chapter 8 – The truth about the watches

Inside the micro-den Dani told the children everything she knew about Dr X and his evil plan. She showed them her own purple watch. She told them all about NASTI. They listened in silence as she spoke.

"Now, can you see how dangerous the watches are?" she said at last.

"So you do want to take them away from us!" said Tiger.

"I'm sorry," Dani said quietly. "I think it might be best …"

Dani didn't want to upset the children. She liked them. She could tell they were clever and brave. But she would never forgive herself if they came to any harm.

"What are you going to do?" said Max. "You can't fight this Dr X all by yourself."

"Max is right," said Cat, "I reckon you could do with some help."

"And I bet we know more about what these watches can do than you," said Ant.

"We can look after ourselves," insisted Tiger.

Soon the four children were all talking at once. Each of them wanted to tell Dani why she should let them keep their amazing watches.

"OK, OK!" Dani held up her hands. "You can keep the watches."

"Yeah!" cried Tiger.

"There's just one thing," said Dani seriously. "I must go back to NASTI," she said.

Dani didn't want to go back to her dark, lonely underground life and the children did their best to convince her to stay. But she knew she had to go. Being inside NASTI was the only way she could keep an eye on Dr X … and make sure the children weren't in any danger. She would keep watching and waiting until the time was right to act. She would make her father proud.

"Well, I'd better be going," sighed Dani.

"I think you're very brave," said Cat.

"So are you kids," said Dani. "But promise me you'll be careful."

"We will," they all promised.

"I'll get messages to you somehow," called Dani as she climbed into the X-pod. "Max, I think I might be able to send holograms to your watch."

A few moments later Dani took off in the X-pod. The children waved to her and she waved back. She found the pod's homing device and sent it on its way back to NASTI.

Later that day ...

"I should never have let you idiots near my precious X-pod!" yelled Dr X. "First you tell me some mad story about it going missing. Then I come in here to find it scratched and dented and, and ..."

Dr X looked like he was about to explode. Plug and Socket just stared at the X-pod. Their minds were as blank as their faces.

"Would you like a nice cup of tea?" asked Plug at last.

It was not a very clever thing to say ...